Ribbons and Moths

Ribbons and Moths

Poems by

Laura Rodley

Cover and interior photos by Laura Rodley
Cover design by Shay Culligan
Author photo by James Rodley

ISBN: 978-1-63980-489-4
Library of Congress Control Number: 2023950988

Kelsay Books
502 South 1040 East, A-119
American Fork, Utah 84003
Kelsaybooks.com

Acknowledgments

Thank you to the following publications, in which versions of these poems previously appeared:

The Aurorean, a Poetry Quarterly: "Harvest"

Orphic Lute: "Crocus"

Ruah: "Grace"

Sanctuary, The Journal of the Massachusetts Audubon Society:
    "End of Fall: Franklin County"

Contents

Mister Cat Reads a Book

Pennies

Look, there's pennies in the river.
Jump in and you will shiver.
Gather enough and you can deliver
a pizza to my house.
If Joe was a giant
he could step down and get them.
If Joe were as big as I
he says he could fly.
He says, "When I am as big as you
there's everything that I can do."
Pennies in the river.
Let's throw in more.
They flip and flop and flip.
Once they're in
we can see them land.
Bright copper pennies
on sludgy river sand.

Kitten

The kitten thinks
he is a magpie,
always snatching
at my silver earring
to put in his nest.

Winter

The pony's coat drips,
her coat an inch thick
under the ice,
parted in the middle
along her spine.
As the ice melts,
steam rises off her back.
She kicks the bucket sharply
with her small hooves,
rat-a-tat-tats
the gray barn boards,
Morse codes
her message: *more hay, now.*
Pony, pony, pony.

Matilda

Matilda, Matilda,
why weren't you called Hilda?
If Hilda you were called
we could say Hildy, Hildy,
how come you are so tall?
But Matildy, Matildy,
that's not fun at all.

First Grade

Gracie's got a wiggler,
a wiggly fat front tooth.
Cheyenne says she loves me,
I say that's not the truth.
Meagan just hit me
so I kicked her back.
Teacher makes us sit down,
apologize, then we can come back.
Liam's got a new dog.
Ben saw a squished frog.
Bridget's moving to Shelburne.
Matthew's got twenty sums to learn.
On Sunday Silas saw his grandpa.
Jason's dad's in trouble with the law.
Joseph's sister got poison ivy.
Ian tried to tie me
up with his jump rope.
He made me bump into Hope.
I play catch with Alex and Noah.
Teacher says it's time to go home,
time to catch the bus.
Shawn just pushed me,
bus driver yells, "Don't fuss!"

Five-Year-Wait

Asparagus green as new grass,
though paler, as underneath a begonia leaf,
tips serrated edges of flavor,
a poor man's delicacy,
a rich man's appetizer,
smothered in butter.

Raccoons

Where do raccoons curl up
and sleep, warm from this sheeting rain,
watering this once dry earth,
are their black noses curled against
their spines or against each other,
is their bushy gray fur
water-repellent, does the
smattering of rain against leaves and rock
say *stay still* to them, *rest*
or *cold, huddle closer,*
as their onyx eyes peer through
the underbrush, keeping watch.

Rabbits

Rabbits are such waiting creatures,
gentle, furry, cuddling
softly in your arms.
Rabbits are such cuddly,
comforting, soft, and warm
pillows to lay your
head next to in a storm.

Mud

Mud comes in uninvited.
Mud leaves big tracks.
Mud speaks a big round hello.
Mud doesn't just come off
the floor; mud must be dried,
then brushed or washed
by mop, sponge or hand.
Mud does not walk away
by itself once it has stepped in.
It's definitely noticeable
and sometimes contagious
like measles.

Moth

I, moth, fly unbidden
into the night.
Under oak leaves I'm hidden.
I'm green and large as your palm
and live just a week.
You can see me
sifting lamp post lights
if you take the time to peek.
My name is luna.
I'm pale as nylons.
My name is luna.
I'll stay by your house
if you leave your light on.
Summer is my time.
I'll lay my eggs and die.
I'm so beautiful
I will not cry.
Luna, luna, luna.

Luna Moth

Traveling

I follow a path
but where it goes,
nobody knows.

Here we travel, travel deep
carrying rainbows
as we sleep.

Feral Cats

Two caramel cats,
one named Pecan,
the other named Pearl,
move their heads tick tock,
tick tock, back and forth
as the dog enters the room.

Dark mahogany spots,
like burls on this wooden floor
are mixed with fur the color
of cheese curl swirls
on their soft coats.

Once scared and starving,
they purr loudly, now brave
and friendly, licking
their paws, barn cats
that now lead
a pampered city life.

Caught

Blue light is caught in the snow.
One-foot down, the ski poles
have cleft tiny altars of light, now reflecting
white and clear from underneath, as though
a sixty-watt bulb shines, a mole's nightlight,
under this three-foot-high offering of snow.

Yard

This yard is wide
and long and deep.
All the moles
are not asleep.
They hold incense
in their toes
and greet worms
burrowing the same path
underneath the tulip bulbs.
It's night, it's night,
but for them,
it's always dark
and this is day.

Milkweed

Little canoe pod rushing
down the air river
full of fairy wings,
soft like rabbit fur, a brown nub
like a miniature soda can tab
holding all the fluff together.

Little spider body-shaped seed,
with a hundred hairy legs.
Milkweed fluff feels like
paintbrush bristles, goose down.
Gather hundreds of the milkweed pods,
pull out the layered wisps,
pack your pillow tight,
dream of flying tonight.

Frog

The road is green mist,
even I am green.
I am hopping, hopping.
My bullfrog throat
is a noisy muffler,
my skin is green and wet.
There are so many trees,
I cannot see the sky.
Yum, a mosquito,
yum, a fly,
watch, I can jump
three feet high.

Burro

Burro waits for us.
She lives in a school bus for a barn.
Her hooves are long.
She brays to keep her temporary owners
safe from harm.
She remembered me a month ago
when I visited to say hello.
She turned her shoulder for me to itch
and when I itched her, her nose
went twitch, twitch, twitch.
She watched me go
and did not bray
to say good-bye.
She only brays to say hello.

Watch Geese

I want a pair of watch geese.
They will be my militant police.
They will guard us with their
powerful wings and peck.
Any intruder will flee the heck
out of our yard
when my watch geese stand guard.

If I Were a Bird

If I were a bird
with a gentle red breast,
and a tiny gray head,
would I be slow
to get out of bed?

Would I fly out the nest,
the wind to test,
glide into fog,
a cloud to ride?

Would I sing
at noon, at dusk,
would my mouth be full
shelling seed husks?

Would my toes curl
round telephone wires,
feeling messages swirl
fifty feet off the ground
high above the traffic sounds?

Would I fly
never faltering
never altering

my route from north to south,
in spring south to north
never changing course?

Would I hide in the sumac
eat its red beard,
peck loose hay seeds
when fields are cleared,

hop three hops before I flew
away from the cat
waiting for me to chew?

Milkweed Fluff

These little wings
must be strong
to float this dark seed along.

Wind helps to carry,
wisps don't tarry,
silent little song.

Beds of sparrow,
autumn's marrow,
milkweed's angel kiss.

Softness
akin to a baby softly touching your face,
a gentle little bliss.

Food From the Kitchen Table as Told by a Puppy

It tastes best if it's
from the kitchen table.
The dog food bowl
is so boring and stable.
I will scarf it down
when they turn their backs
if I am able.

Bad Habits

My owner's other dog taught
them bad habits. She did not give
full obedience to them but to smells,
nose to gravel—chipmunk,
coyote, fox, salamander;
I am different.
My legs are longer, I like grapes
better, I see chipmunks that
she missed. Her eyes were bigger
but her eyes were in her nose,
the ground her map, tracks
her tributaries. And so,
I can walk across, head held high.

I confess I like caterpillars
but I will not stoop to bark at them,
nor will I try to eat their furry backs
as I heard my owner's other dog tried.
I confess I may not have as good
a schnoz as my owner's last dog
but I have better hearing.
My owners say that whistle
in the distance
is a train in Charlemont.
What is a train?
A noisy snake?

Summer Mischief

Children are sleeping,
crickets are cheeping,
mother's sewing on the porch,
daddy's snoring,
his boat is tied to the mooring.
Elves tickle the caged rabbits
until they sneeze.
Elves chop up a spinach leaf,
eat it as a salad, rattle chitins
of the chinch bugs,
bother the cats,
pull their tails,
hop on their backs,
hold on until the fur loosens,
as the cats flee through the breezeway
cut into the bottom of the kitchen door.

Pony

Her hooves leave tiny dancing
prancing prints around the house.
Her prints are small, and perfect,
like a burro's.
She knows how to scoot
under the wire fence at night,
chivy back in again in the morning.
She pretends it wasn't her
who pulled up the carrots,
ate the leaves
off the sunflowers,
trampled down the wicket fence
protecting big fat pumpkins.
She stares at me now
from where she's tied,
begging me to let her loose,
innocence in her eyes.

Moon

Where is the moon to hold it all,
that glamorous spotlight careening
from the heavens and how will
we know who is waiting
while God sits up there
knitting a silk scarf for
the sun; he's constantly
knitting, as each time the
shoulders of the sun reach
for the sweater, pouf, it's
smoke, a dust storm, a
meteor shower and God is up
there again, wondering about
using yak fiber or angora fiber,
maybe camel, and the sun
rises obliviously, clocking in
once again, always three minutes
late, so the years turn and the
days grow longer and the moon
can squirrel herself away
in the minty mist of morning sky.

Making Quilts

Fabric on the chairs
hung over doors
boxes of cloth stacked
across the floors.

What color, what color,
how much, how wide
how do wings look
when a swallow hides?

Crocus

Little wine cup
holding its yellow pollen
up to the sun.

Purple, yellow, white,
drink me, drink me.
Amber bees fresh from snow dreams
hear and dip into the cup,
stagger out, legs packed yellow,
almost too heavy to fly.

Local Farmer

Purposely sowing the tiny seed in
furrows shallow to fit the need
of people waiting for their salad,
or gardens too small for onions,
potatoes and turnips, the farmer
waits, hope kept in check by weather,
clouds and rain, until weeks pass
and it's time to pick again the bounty
of generous soil and seeds' rebirth,
a farmer's reward for working the uncertain,
yet prepared, palette of crumbly black earth.

Amelia and Maisie Burch at Diemand Farm in Wendell MA

Snapping Turtle

Hiding, staying still, the snapping turtle
looks like a large chunk of gray granite.
Sure glad I didn't step on it.
Look, he pokes out his head real slow.
Are we someone he wants to know?
See him waddle into the grass.
He can't go very fast.
What a silly nose, small gold eyes,
he's making mud pies!
Stay back, don't linger,
he might chomp your finger.

Apparel

Does the dog wear boots?
Does the dog wear mittens?
Does the dog have a muffler?
Where is the cat's sweater?
Where are her earmuffs?
Where is the horse's jacket
the scarf for her long neck,
where is the overcoat
for the rabbit, sunglasses for the duck,
the snowshoes for chickens?
Have you seen them?

End of Fall: Franklin County

Snow is on the ground and local
farms are winding down.
Paddy Flat in Ashfield still
has squash; butternut,
delicata, hubbard and acorn.
Red Fire from Granby
has lettuce, spinach and other picks.
What about cabbages and potatoes
from the good farm *Enterprise,*
rutabagas, and those rounded beauties,
turnips, tiny worlds unto their
own; cut into their purple skins
and you'll find the gold within
when it's cold outside and blood is thin.
And then the carrots from *Picadilly*
and huckleberry potatoes with red skins
and flesh from *Donovan,*
grown high in the hills
where winter first begins.

Thea Mundy and two-year-old Jersey Janet
at the Strolling of the Heifers in Brattleboro, VT
representing Putney School as a sophomore.

Grace

Gray squirrel mantled
with crust of snow
cracks open the sunflower seed,
the prayer he's saying
in his cupped hands,
thank you for this tiny seed,
oh God, thank you for my
fur, oh thank you for the
breath in my nose,
his tail fluffing out in
the buffeting wind.

Harvest

We did not mow down the comfrey;
the goldenrod pushed it over.
Now the milkweed stands chest high,
food for orange monarchs come
to rest like moving rings upon each
minute yellow flower.

They fly their orange veils
through the raindrops.
Their veils do not break;
the rain breaks around them,
lets them fly through,
call back the September winds
when they coast through dust and clouds
to Mexico to sleep on sand.

Kitty

Listen quickly, little kitty,
are there any mices?
I have traveled hard the road
to quince and quosh,
have you any vices?
Maybe catnip to name one,
kitty litter to name two.
Tell me, little kitty,
haven't you any chores to do?

Llama

This brown llama has long ears punched like
toll cards, the exit she entered.
You can see the sun through the holes,
her eyes brown and liquid,
her cloven hooves sharp and quick,
her fleece long and silky.
How strange to be a Peruvian llama
here in Hawley. Did she fly,
or travel in the belly of a boat,
her cria born here on American soil,
with long white ears, a bunny tail, and
miles ahead of her to traverse the trail.

Acorn

I'm an acorn.
No, I'm not.
But, let's pretend
that I've got
arms stretching with leaves,
bark on my knees,
my nose pressed flat, and
hands touching sky
as I stand
forty feet high.
What am I?

Friendships

Sarah's got a new Dad.
Sam has got a new Mom.
Manda's Dad doesn't get along
with her Mom.
She sees him only on Sundays.
I see Savannah on Tuesdays
when she stays with her Mom;
Monday, Tuesday, Wednesday,
Thursday, Friday.
I see Jennifer Saturday.
We play runaway.
She wants to run away
to visit her Dad.
He left her Mom.
Her Mom's always so sad.
Her Dad's got her brother.
They don't see much of each other.
Caitlin's staying with her aunt
so Jennifer and I can't
play runaway with her.
Summer's almost over.
Crystal's got a boyfriend,
and tomorrow Meagan goes home.
Looks like Sunday
I'll play all alone.

Haven

The ground is trodden flat
with horses' heavy feet,
the black mud dried and baked
by early summer heat.
The short-cropped grass
smells acridly sharp and sweet.
The path I walk
is my calm silent treat,
this path the horses have
widened coming in to eat.

View

The orange glow of the city shines
high into the sky, an ember.
From this lookout tower
we see the house lights
as stars in an attainable galaxy,
a galaxy we drive
through in the daylight
to buy our bread.

Jim and Cinnamon on Their Way

About the Author

Pushcart Prize winner Laura Rodley is a septuple Pushcart Prize nominee, quintuple Best of the Net nominee. She edited and published *As You Write It, A Franklin County Anthology I–VI*, and *As You Write It Lucky 7*, seven collections of memoir from seniors she taught at the Gill Montague Senior Center for fourteen years. Latest books are *Turn Left at Normal* by Big Table Publishing, *Counter Point* by Prolific Press, a fictional story about a girl named Marie who disguised herself as a pirate on the real-life *Whydah* that floundered and sank off the coast of Cape Cod Massachusetts on April 26, 1717.